Little I

Written by Rozanne Lanczak Williams
Created by Sue Lewis
Illustrated by Patty Briles

Creative Teaching Press

Little Miss Jill

© 2002 Creative Teaching Press, Inc.
Written by Rozanne Lanczak Williams
Illustrated by Patty Briles
Project Manager: Sue Lewis
Project Director: Carolea Williams

Published in the United States of America by:
Creative Teaching Press, Inc.
P.O. Box 2723
Huntington Beach, CA 92647-0723

CTP 3236

Who will hit the ball?

Jill will!

Who will kick it in the net?

Jill will!

Who will swim
and win the race?

Little Miss Jill will!

Who will win this?

We all will!

Create your own book!

Following the sentence pattern in the book,
write a story about yourself or a friend.

Words in *Little Miss Jill*

Short *i*	High-Frequency Words	Other
Little	who	ball
Miss	the	net
Jill	and	race
this	we	best
will	all	team
hit		spirit
it		
kick		
in		
win		
swim		